Feed Sack Rich

*MacKenzie H.
Memories of
home!
Cathy Bartley*

Written by
Cathy Bartley

Illustrations by
Christopher Epling

Text and Illustrations Copyright 2016
Cathy Bartley
Publishing Rights: Heart-Sewn Publishing
Publishing Date: September 2016

Author: Cathy Bartley
Illustrator: Christopher Epling
Designer: Epling Illustrations

ISBN: 978-0-9893574-2-5
1.) Children's Literature, 2.) Kentucky Culture
3.) Eastern Kentucky History
2.)Family Focused
3.)Bartley, Cathy

First Edition
10 9 8 7 6 5 4 3 2

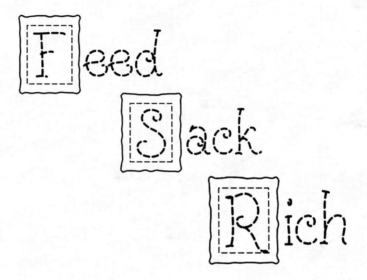

Feed Sack Rich

Written by
Cathy Bartley

Illustrations by
Christopher Epling

Dedication

Feed Sack Rich is dedicated to all the hardworking families and friends who united together and survived during the difficult times of the 1950's in Pike County, Kentucky.

Feed Sack Rich
An Introduction

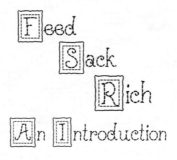

Should a passer-by chance to venture into the heartland of Marrowbone Creek, a region embedded deeply in Pike County, Kentucky, he would discover a rolling valley that formed between beautiful green mountains abundant with voluminous towering trees. Rising high on all sides, and rooted-in so deeply, this lofty forest holds such a spacious captivity that it only leaves a small opening for a shallow creek and a country road that meanders from the mouth to the head of a hollow known as Dry Fork. That was my home. Born and reared in that valley, I was surrounded by kin folk who provided a safety net of nurturing and love. And that love has made me who I am today.

My mommy used to tell the story of how I came into this world one hot July evening on the tail end of 1940's. Mommy had given birth to my brother, Roger Lee, fourteen months earlier, so, I guess she wasn't worried about having that second child. Mommy and Daddy had saved up three hundred dollars to pay the hospital and doctor's bill when it was her time to go. My daddy had worked many nights in the Henry Clay Coal Mine to rake and scrape up that much money. And Mommy knew her time was getting close, and so did my Mammaw Lucy and my Aunt Lola, who lived next door, and kept a watch on my mommy while my daddy was pulling another ten hour shift loading coal at the Henry Clay Mine. That was the night I decided to enter this world.

My mommy called for my Aunt Lola to come quickly, yelling, "It's time for the baby!" My Mammaw Lucy scrambled up the hill to Mommy's bed, having given birth to twelve children, she knew exactly what to do. My mammaw and aunt sent for Maudie Ratliff, a midwife, who lived at the head of the hollow, to help with the delivery. In another thirty minutes, I was born, Mammaw Lucy, gave me a spank, I screamed, and became the newest member in the Bartley family.

My Grandpa Sparriel, having worked his shift in the coal mine, came home to a new granddaughter. Being the head of the family, he wanted to make sure everything was alright with my mommy and me. He decided to make a trip to the Henry Clay Mining Company doctor.

Doctor Kostleman, a German who had escaped Hitler's Regime, and made his way to the mountains of Marrowbone Creek, jumped into the truck with my Papaw Sparriel, and made a home visit. Dr. Kostleman examined my mommy, then picked me up by the heels and replied, "She's about nine pounds." He filled out a birth certificate and charged my mommy and daddy forty-five dollars. Jokes were always made throughout the family saying, "I was the cheapest child in the family."

My Mommy gave birth to seven children, but I was the only one born at home. I always felt special because my Mammaw Lucy and a kind neighbor were the first two persons to touch me. I'm sure my mommy laid me right beside her, where I could feel the warmth of her body for the first hours of my life. Mommy said that my first glance of my daddy was when he was covered with coal dust, with a big smile across his face. And if I could only remember the first time I heard my daddy's voice, I'm certain that my heart melted, and at that moment, he became the center of my life.

I remember so vividly how we made a living by the sweat of the brow, were deeply devoted to our family, and believed in earning an honest living with the help from the Lord above.

I hope you enjoy the first of many stories that I remember as a child growing up on Dry Fork, where hard times often knocked at our door, like the north wind they entered, but through our love for each other those same hardships were driven out as fast as they came. We were a family!!! We stood strong!!!

Feed Sack Rich

Written by
Cathy Bartley

Illustrations by
Christopher Epling

"Aunt Lola, are you home?" I began to yell as I opened up the squeaky screen door that led to my aunt's kitchen. There was always a good home-baked aroma that captivated my senses as soon as I entered her well-worn, yet clean kitchen, regardless of the time of day.

Aunt Lola called from the back bedroom, "In here, Cathy!" I followed the sound of her voice, stuck my head around the corner of the door, and said, "Mommy sent me after some fresh churned butter." Aunt Lola spoke as she folded some colored material on her bed.

There were sheets with patterns of bright yellow and brown flowers all neatly laid out on her bed. "OK, I have a fresh mold in the ice box." Then she said, "But, first, look at this material!" "Do you like it?" I replied, "Oh, it's so pretty." Is that for me?"

Aunt Lola exclaimed, "Yes, I've been saving this for you! Now, before school starts, I want you to come get the material, and take it to Marilyn Thacker so she can sew a new dress for you and Faye."

Marilyn lived a couple houses down from my family, and was known as our local seamstress. I said, 'I'll tell Mommy." Aunt Lola remarked, "Be sure you do! Don't forget ." then she declared, "We better get that butter if you are planning on having it for supper!"

I felt as proud as a peacock as I held the churned butter, wrapped tightly in waxed paper, and headed home. I loved my aunt for saving the material from sacks of feed that she bought weekly at Earl Johnson's Store for her cows and pigs.

She made sure she got to the store early when the feed delivery truck arrived every Thursday. All the local women tried to be the first in line to get the prettiest, colorful feed sacks. Aunt Lola always picked out the prettiest patterns as they were thrown from the back of the truck.

7.

After the animals had eaten all the feed, Aunt Lola would cut the feed sack until the material was a huge square. Then she would wash the sack, hang it on the line to dry, and iron it flatly. She would save those sacks for weeks in order to get enough material for my sister, Faye and me.

Aunt Lola, like all my family members, helped each other survive the trials of life. My mommy and daddy had three children in 1956, my brother, Roger Lee, my sister, Faye and me. Times were hard, pockets were empty, and we learned to count our pennies by saving as much as we could.

We planted a big garden, then harvested and canned the food we grew. We raised hogs, chickens, and cows, and an old mule was always needed to plow the fields.

I remember it was in the last days of August, the sun beamed down hot and steamy on my bare feet as I walked down the old dirt road that I had traveled so many times.

I knew every rock, bump, or sink hole in this dusty road that meandered by a shallow creek, snaking its way down a hollow nestled deep in the mountains in Pike County, known as Dry Fork. This was my home; with family and loved ones all nestled together in a valley abound with tall trees, fertile soil, and a firm belief in Jesus Christ.

I was careful not to drop the fresh churned butter that my mommy had sent me after. I was so scared that the butter would melt if I didn't hurry.

My daddy, after working all day in the Henry Clay Coal Mine, loved hot cornbread and butter for supper. And if there was one thing that I'd learned from my mommy, it was, "A hard working man deserves a good meal after ten hours under the ground."

Still, I could not help gazing at the nearby hills where tall, lanky oaks and sycamore trees filled in the mountains like flower arrangements in a pot. The hills were alive with color, showing off that summer green with bits of gold, orange, and brown sprinkled throughout the mountains, giving the peaks and valleys a tint of the fall to come.

15.

Pretty soon school would begin. I would be a second grader at the Carmen Grade School, located at the mouth of the hollow. Just a one room school, but three grades were taught by Mrs. Mabel Adkins.

I heard Mommy talking to Daddy the other day, stating that some of the neighbors living near the school had been scrubbing the desks, outside toilets, and floors. I couldn't wait to see all my friends who lived on the hollow, or nearby in other hollows on that first day of school.

Well, I was nearing my home, still holding on to the fresh butter, and decided to stop day dreaming. After all, Mama depended on me, since I was the oldest girl. I reckon I had a rightful place in the family to be a guide for my younger siblings.

Mommy had supper on the table. Daddy had just bathed in the big round tub in the back yard, with water that had been warmed earlier in the day by the hot sun. Daddy sat first at our family table wearing a shiny, clean face, starched and ironed khaki clothes, and neatly combed hair that had been slicked back with Woodbury hair oil.

I would never have known that he had been in a coal mine if not for the coal dust under his nails, and blisters on his hands.

Mommy carried a huge bowl of fresh green beans to the table, followed by a platter of fried potatoes. There was fatback pork, crispy and tasty, along with a fresh pone of cornbread, and Aunt Lola's fresh churned butter.

Then I poured us all a large glass of milk. This time of day was always special, because all the family was there, gathered together to eat and share the good things that had happened that day.

My daddy took a large piece of hot cornbread and began slapping a chunk of fresh butter on the bite he was planning to take. That's when I remembered what my Aunt Lola had told me, "Feed Sack Dresses!" Mommy, I exclaimed, "Aunt Lola has saved some pretty feed sacks for Faye and me."

"It's so pretty, Mommy, all bright colors, with flowers
that look like wild mountain bouquets. Mommy said,
"Ya' aunt cares about you girls." "And you can't find
any better material for making dresses for school." "So,
Cathy, we'll take care of that tomorrow. Now, eat your
supper. We still have the dishes to do."

When supper was over, Mommy placed a huge pot of water on the coal stove to warm for the dish water. We scraped all the food from the bowls and plates, and gave the scraps to the dogs and hogs.

While I waited for the water to heat up, I took the hogs' scraps out to the feed house, added water and middlings to make a thick soup, and carried the bucket full of food to the hungry waiting hogs.

As soon as I poured the slop into the trough, the hogs lapped, snorted, and smacked, and gobbled up their long awaited meal.

Back in the kitchen, the steamed water had been poured into a dish pan full of suds and dirty dishes. Mommy said, "You wash and I'll rinse." I loved washing dishes with my mommy. As I washed the bowls and plates, I kept thinking about the pretty feed sack material, and the dress I would wear on the first day of school.

I looked at Mommy, and asked her if she had any ideas about how Marilyn should sew our new dresses? Mommy said, "I'll get the new Sears & Roebuck Catalog, and find a dress pattern that will fit you best. Then tear out the page, and let you take it to Marilyn, along with the feed sacks."

29.

I felt so lucky when Mommy told me that. Some might think we were near to being poor, money was as scarce as hen's teeth, but look what I had around me.

There was my Aunt Lola looking out for me, Mommy choosing, a pattern from a mail order catalog, and a neighbor named Marilyn, who was so gifted that she could just look at a picture, then take her old Singer foot- pedaled sewing machine, and whip-up a dress that looked as good as any store bought design.

And, not only that, I would look fresh and new on the first day of school. I could just picture me walking through that old wooden school door, as Mrs. Mabel Adkins held that worn out bell, ringing, "Ding Dong, Ding Dong!" and feeling on top of the world when I found the second grade row and took my seat.

I got so excited that I could barely fall asleep just thinking about that first day of school and my new feed sack dress. But while listening to the sound of crickets chirping through the night, and the touch of a gentle breeze flowing through a screened window, I was soon lulled to sleep.

33.

Early the next morning, after Daddy had gone to the coal mine, Mommy started looking through the Sears & Roebuck Catalog to find a picture of a little girl's dress that she thought would suit me. After thumbing through several pages, she decided on a full tailed skirt and matching blouse.

Mommy showed me her choice as I ate my biscuits and gravy. She said, "Cathy, after breakfast, go to your Aunt Lola's , gather up the feed sack material, and bring it to me, so I can look it over before we take it to Marilyn's."

I quickly finished my last bite of her homemade biscuit, topped with fresh crab apples Mommy had cooked that morning. I headed out the door, and began running to my aunt's house.

Aunt Lola was an early riser, too. She was busy cleaning up her kitchen and preparing some fresh green beans for lunch. My Aunt Lola's husband, whom we called Uncle Mann, expected three home cooked meals a day. I can never remember a time when there wasn't food on Aunt Lola's table.

37.

"Aunt Lola," I began to say, still breathless from running so hard from my house, "Mommy wants the feed sacks so we can get Marilyn to sew me a skirt and blouse." "A skirt and blouse," she replied, "Boy, you are going to look like a movie star on the first day of school!"

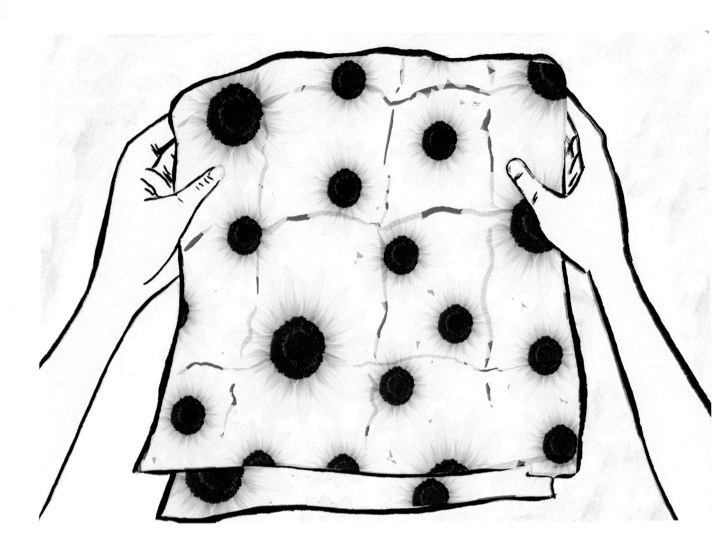

I just laughed as I followed her into her back bedroom, where the feed sack material was neatly stacked. Aunt Lola placed the stacks of material in my hand. I couldn't help but admire the bright yellow material with huge sunflowers, decked out with brown centers, creating a richness only seen in the fall of the year. Oh, how I loved that pattern.

Before I left Aunt Lola's bedroom, still holding the feed sacks, she looked at me and said, "Do you need any buttons for your skirt and blouse?" I said, "Yes!" Then Aunt Lola went to her top dresser drawer, and pulled out a little jar full of buttons she had collected from her old garments.

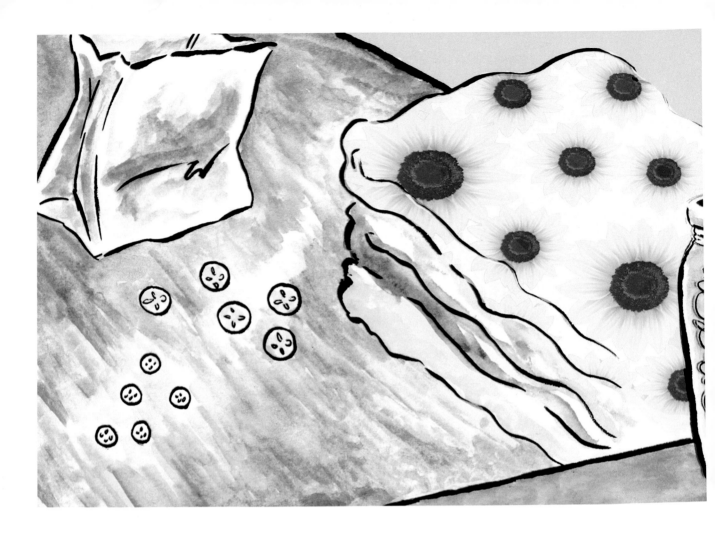

She found five bright, yellow buttons for my blouse and skirt, then five white ones for my sister, Faye. She located a tiny, brown paper bag, dropped the buttons in, and then placed it between the feed sack material.

41.

I held the material tightly as I walked home, making sure not to drop it in the dusty road before Mommy had a chance to see how beautiful it was.

Mommy met me at the kitchen screen door, then took the feed sack material, and laid it on the table. She unfolded it, to make sure there was enough yards to make my sister and me an outfit each. Mommy loved the fabric, too.

She hollered for my sister, Faye, who just turned four, and told her she would go with me to Marilyn's. She refolded the material, placed the torn page from the catalog inside the feed sacks, and handed it back to me. She said, "Take this to Marilyn, tell her what we want, and ask her if she has time to make your outfit this week."

My Mommy knew that Marilyn Thacker had a family, too; with four children and her husband all living in a three room house, trying to make a living on a miner's pay. Marilyn, too, collected feed sacks for her girls, and sewed them up, like the rest of the neighbors who lived on Dry Fork, and made do with what they had.

Marilyn was threading the bobbin in her old, Singer, sewing machine when Faye and I arrived at her house with our feed sacks, picture, and buttons. I knocked on her door, and waited on her front porch until she told us to come in.

I showed her the material, and the picture Mommy had picked out of the catalog. Marilyn said, "Well, I'm sure I can sew this, all I need is your measurements." She said, "Maybe you girls have grown a little this summer."

She took out her worn tape measure, began stretching here and there, and writing down numbers after each measurement. Then she said, "Finished, girls! Tell your Mommy that I will do my best to get this finished this week!"

We left, feeling on top of the world, gabbing all the way home about how pretty we would look in our new outfit. Although my sister, Faye didn't go to school yet, she would sometimes visit my school for special occasions, so Mommy wanted her to look her best.

49.

The next Saturday, Marilyn stopped my daddy on his way home from work, and told him our outfits were finished. When I heard the news, I couldn't wait to get my new skirt and blouse.

Mommy gave me a dime and a quarter and said, "Ask Marilyn how much she needs for sewing your feed sack outfits." I said, "Sure will!" Then off I went down the road to the Thacker's.

Marilyn and her family were eating supper when I knocked on the door. She asked me if I wanted to eat, but I said, "No, thank you!" I told her Mommy sent me after our outfits. Marilyn went to her sewing machine, and brought back the most beautiful skirt and blouse that I had ever seen.

She said, "I'm sure it will fit, but let me know if it doesn't." I held out my hand, and offered her the coins in my sweaty palm. Marilyn took a quarter, and said, "That will be enough! Just take that dime back home with you!" I thanked her, and quickly took the outfits, and headed home.

I ran through the yard, bounced up the steps, and saw that Mommy and Daddy were sitting on the front porch. Mommy said, "Go try your outfit on; let's see if it will fit." I ran to my room, stripped off my sweaty clothes, and slowly slipped my skirt over my head, down to my waist, and then I buttoned it.

"Perfect fit." I placed my arms through the sleeves of my new blouse, and buttoned it! "Perfect Fit." I went to the old dresser in Mommy's bedroom, looked through the mirror, and could not take my eyes away from the beautiful reflection I saw.

I danced, twirled around, posed, and laughed with excitement. Then I ran to the front porch, strutting prissily, and showed off my outfit to Mommy and Daddy. They, too, loved it. Mommy said, "I told you that feed sacks make pretty outfits." Daddy agreed. My sister, Faye tried her skirt and blouse on, although she was a little chubby, the whole outfit suited her to a tee.

That night Daddy showed my brother, Roger Lee, the pair of Wrangler blue jeans and red checked, long, sleeved shirt he had bought at the Henry Clay Mining Company Store. Then Mommy sat down, and ordered my brother and me a pair of shoes from that same Sears & Roebuck catalog.

My brother got a sturdy pair of brown, lace-up, high top shoes; mine were brown and white saddle oxfords. As soon as the shoes came in the mail, we would be ready for the first day of school.

That day did arrive. I'll never forget that September morning. Roger Lee and I were up at the crack of dawn, ate our breakfast, and then got ready for school. The Carmen Grade School was located a mile down the road, and usually we just walked. But, on this particular day in September, it was raining cats and dogs.

Mommy didn't want us to get wet, so, she told us to catch a ride with a coal hauler who trucked coal out of Dry Fork. Mommy and Daddy knew all the coal truck drivers who hauled the coal out of our hollow, especially Leeman Adkins. He drove a converted, old, Army truck, with a bed on the back, that was used to haul coal from a nearby tipple.

Mommy gave us a new pencil and a writing tablet while we waited for our ride on our little front porch. Then we saw Leeman's truck. Mommy waved him down. He stopped, and we climbed inside the cab. Mommy told me to take care, and not get coal dust on my new outfit. We waved good-bye to our mommy, and headed off to school.

Leeman slowed down when we approached the school. After stopping the truck, Roger Lee and I climbed out, ran across the road, and crossed a narrow wooden bridge, built over a creek, that gave a pathway to our school yard.

It was still pouring down the rain, so there were no children playing on the swings. As we scurried closer to the schoolhouse, the bell began to ring, "Ding! Dong!" We opened the door, and walked in. Oh!! That wonderful feeling of seeing all my friends, especially in my new feed sack outfit, I felt that I had the world by the tail!

Many school days came and went after that first day when I was a second grader at the Carmen Grade School in 1956, and my feed sack outfits were sewn time and time again. Some folks might think we were feed sack poor, but I'm obliged to differ. I couldn't imagine being reared any differently.

That one room school and my feed sack clothes were part of my life when I was a child, growing up on Dry Fork. I had a Mommy and Daddy who believed in hard work , honoring your roots, and offering a helping hand to loved ones in need.

My feed sack outfits, not only provided me with needed clothing, but also gave me the security of knowing I was nestled in the arms of a loving family. And that made me "Feed Sack Rich!"

Feed Sack Rich

Uncle Mann and Aunt Lola Bartley and their son John.

Left to right. Back row: Manis Hylton, Cathy's uncle. Second row, left to right: Annisteen Bartley, Cathy's mom holding her sister Faye, Herbert Lee Bartley, Cathy's daddy, Matthew and Laritta (Pet) Hylton, Cathy's grandparents, Roger Lee (her brother), and Cathy.

The Thackers, Marilyn and George and their baby.

Roger Lee

Mom and Daddy

Cathy

Author Biography

Born and raised on Dry Fork of Marrow-bone, located in Pike County, Kentucky, I learned early in life that hard times came to all, but it was the way we dealt with these difficult times that made the difference in success and failure. I was taught that education was a must, family-loyalty was essential, and striving to work and become a better person was instilled in every child's mind.

I graduated from Hellier High School, attended the University of Pikeville four years, and completed my graduate work through Morehead State University. I majored in elementary education, but also took several courses in English, Composition, and Literature. I taught elementary school for thirty one years and focused on teaching Language Arts and Creative Writing to students.

I'm very proud of my first book ,"Feed Sack Rich", a true story of my family facing hardships and how we dealt with them when I was a small child. This story, as well as my other written works, stems from memories of my childhood and my teaching experiences. Life is the best teacher!!

- Cathy Bartley

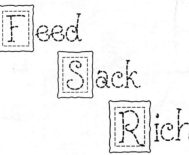

Feed Sack Rich